THE
WHISTLER
AND OTHER STORIES

**Reading
and
Exercise
Series**

Reading & Exercise Series

THE
WHISTLER
AND OTHER STORIES

Adaptations and exercises by Jean N. Dale
Edited by Willard D. Sheeler

ELS Publications
A Division of W.E.R.A., Inc.
5761 Buckingham Parkway
Culver City, CA 90230

Cover design by Mark Fristad

Text design by John Eccles

Illustrated by Loren Weeks

Acknowledgment is made for permission to print
adaptations of the following:

"What Difference?" by Edwin T. Cornelius, III
"A Work of Art" by Anton Chekhov

ISBN 0-89285-050-7

preface

The Whistler is the first of six books in the *Reading and Exercise Series,* designed for students of English as a second language. *The Whistler* contains five original stories and one adaptation, *A Work of Art,* by Anton Chekhov. Each story is followed by exercise material, an integral part of the book, which can be profitably used to help the student improve his reading skills. As an aid to the teacher, a checklist of principal grammatical structures and vocabulary listings is provided in *The Whistler* for correlating this book with basic classroom text-books.

The *Reading and Exercise Series* is designed for use as supplementary material to most basic textbooks. Students using *Welcome to English* will find that *The Whistler* is appropriate for Books 1 and 2. The stories are prepared for students working at the elementary and intermediate levels and are thematically of interest to adults and young adults.

The tape recordings that accompany this series provide a valuable opportunity for the student to hear language in use. The tapes present a variety of native American voices, both male and female.

introduction
for the teacher

The Whistler consists of six stories with accompanying exercises which are an integral part of the book. It is designed to be used as supplementary reading material either in conjunction with *Welcome to English* or with other basic texts.

Supplementary reading material may be used to reinforce known structures, or simply to provide enjoyment and to give the student a sense of accomplishment that will encourage him to read more extensively. Supplementary readings are generally offered without time pressure and without detailed discussion of the language structure. The readings should not be so difficult for the student that they produce frustration.

To this end, we have limited the vocabulary load and used only a selected number of grammatical structures.

Vocabulary. Following each story, certain words from the reading selection are isolated and defined contextually. Many are illustrated.

This vocabulary section can be used to pre-teach vocabulary items before having the students read the story. It is a matter of the teacher's preference and experience whether to pre-teach vocabulary or to wait until after the reading and work with only those items causing difficulty. Many words which are likely to cause difficulty are explained or defined within the story itself. The illustrations, too, can be an aid in explaining certain vocabulary items.

The words selected for study are those which are "new" in the sense that they have not occurred in preceding lessons of the basic textbook series *Welcome to English.* Word lists, broken down by parts of speech are at the back of the book together with a cumulative word list.

Structure. Structures used in the readings are those presented in *Welcome to English, Books 1 and 2.* For teachers using this series, the following table shows at what point the stories in *The Whistler* should be assigned for reading.

	Welcome to English, Book 2
Next Monday	Unit 1
May 23	Unit 2
What Difference?	Unit 3
The Beautiful Young Spy	Unit 4
A Work of Art	Unit 5
The Whistler	Unit 6

For teachers who wish to use this reader with other textbooks, a checklist has been provided which lists the principal structures used in the various stories. (These are cumulative from one story to the next.) A study of this table will enable the teacher to determine when a reading may be introduced.

Exercises. In addition to the vocabulary section, there are a number of exercises which will help the student improve his reading skills. In the main, these are "grammar" exercises which focus attention on the meaning and use of function words such as noun determiners and prepositions; on the recognition and composition of noun phrase constituents; and on the processes of conjoining and subordination. The grammatical topic of each exercise is listed in the table of contents.

There is an answer key at the back of the book. Complete sentences are given as answers to comprehension questions. However, in order to develop natural conversation skills, the use of short answers is recommended for oral work. Possible answers are given for the comprehension sections, though a variety of alternatives will be acceptable.

Conversation. Each story may be used as a vehicle for conversation practice. After reading a story at least twice, listening to it on tape and working the exercises, students will become familiar with all the details. They will be able to talk with some confidence about the situations, and about the characters and their motivations.

Tape Recordings. The six stories are recorded, along with selected exercises. The recorded exercises are indicated in the table of contents by the following symbol: □. The students should read and listen to the story and then do the written exercises as homework or classwork *before* listening to the exercises on tape. They will then be able to follow the tape easily, giving their own written responses orally at the appropriate times from open books. The tape voice gives the cue, the student responds; then there is confirmation and a second opportunity for the student to respond. The tape voice gives all necessary instructions.

The dictation exercise may be a new experience. The first instruction from the tape voice is for the student to close the book. Each sentence is given once at normal speed, a second time in phrases (while the student writes), and a third time at normal speed. The tape voice then instructs the student to stop the tape, open the book, check the work, and recopy any sentences containing errors.

contents

II What do you remember?

III Practice with the prepositions 'into' and 'in'
   A. Read these sentences.
   B. Repeat the sentences in Part A.
   □ C. Fill in the right preposition.

□ IV Questions with 'did,' 'was,' 'were' and short answers

□ V Subordinate clauses (subordinators 'when' and 'while')

□ VI Modification: noun + '-ing' verb

□ VII Prepositions: review

READING

next monday

"Where are my army shoes? Do you know, Mary?" Frank was standing at the open door of the bedroom.

"Your what?" Mary was in the kitchen.

"My army shoes!"

"Oh, Frank. Who knows? I certainly don't know," Mary said. "Why do you want them now after all these years?"

"I want to wear them with my uniform, of course." Frank was walking into the kitchen. He was wearing his old brown uniform and he was having a good time. "Look! I'm wearing it—after twenty-eight years. I need my shoes, too. I'm going to see my old army friends tonight, you know. The party is at eight o'clock. I want to wear my uniform."

Mary was looking at the uniform and she was laughing. "Well, Frank, you're getting a little fat! Where was your uniform?"

"It was with some other old clothes. Now I have all these things, but where are my shoes? I need the right shoes. I don't want to wear these.

"What's this? Look at this old yellow piece of paper. It was in my pocket."

Mary was looking at the piece of paper with him. "Look at the date, Frank. This is from a shoe repairman. This is a ticket for your old shoes!"

"Yes, it is!" Frank said. "Now I remember. The shoe repairman has the shoes for my uniform. He was going to fix them for me. My shoes are still there!"

Mary was laughing. "They certainly aren't there now! They certainly aren't there after twenty-eight years!"

"I'm going to see the old man," said Frank. "I have some time now. I'm going to get my shoes!"

In a few minutes, Frank was in his car. He was still wearing his uniform and he was going to see the shoe repairman. He was thinking about his days in the army. "My army job was near here. I never come here now. The buildings are old. It's all very old. Is this the right street? Yes, I think it is.

"The shoe repairman is a very old man now. Is he still living? Is he still here? He's very old now—and I'm old, too. Twenty-eight years!"

The old shoe repairman was still there! He was working. He was repairing a shoe. The old man was talking, but there weren't any other people there!

Frank said, "Hello. I think you have my old shoes. You were going to fix them for me. My name is on this ticket."

"Oh, yes, I remember," said the old man. "I have them. They're here. They're in the back room. I repair a lot of army shoes, you know."

Frank wasn't listening to him. Frank was looking at the old man but he was still thinking about his days in the army.

Then the old man said, "Yes, yes, here they are. Yes, I have them. Yes, I'm going to fix them, too. I'm very busy, you know. I repair a lot of army shoes. I'm always busy. I never have enough time. Here are your shoes, but they aren't ready now. Come back next Monday!"

EXERCISES

I Do you know these words from the story?

uniform   wear   said
pocket   ticket

A. Read these sentences:

1. Frank's *wearing* his old army clothes.
   He's wearing his army *uniform*.

2. An old yellow piece of paper was in the *pocket* of his uniform.
   It was a shoe repair *ticket*.

3. He's going to take the ticket to the shoe repairman.
   He wants to get his shoes from the shoe repairman.

B. Write these sentences from dictation:

1. A fireman wears a uniform.
   His clothes keep him dry.

2. Nurses wear white clothes.
   Their white uniforms have pockets.

3. Take your old shoes to a shoe repairman.
   Get a shoe repair ticket.

C. These sentences use direct speech. Copy them.

(Said is the past form of say.)

1. Frank said, "I'm going to wear my uniform tonight."
2. Mary said, "You're getting fat."
3. "I'm going to get my shoes," said Frank.
4. "The shoes aren't there now," said Mary.

II What do you remember?

Answer the questions.

1. Why was Mary laughing at Frank?
2. What time was the party going to begin?
3. Who was going to be at the party?
4. What was in Frank's pocket?
5. What's a shoe repair ticket for?
6. Was Mary going to go get the shoes? Who was?
7. What was the shoe repairman doing?
8. How many years were Frank's shoes at the shoe repairman's?
9. Were the shoes ready for Frank?
10. When were the shoes going to be ready?

EXERCISES continued

III Practice with the preposition 'at'

A. Action drill (use students' names)

1. Student A stands at the table. Student B stands at the door.

   Class repeat: Student B is at the door. Student A is at the table.

2. Student B walks to the teacher's desk. Stands there.

   Class repeat: Now Student B is at the teacher's desk, but Student A is still at the table.

3. Student B walks to the window. Stands there.

   Class repeat: Now Student B is at the window, but Student A is still at the table.

4. Student B walks to the blackboard. Stands there.

Class repeat: Now Student B is at the blackboard, but Student A is still at the table.

Repeat the drill with other students. Substitute other positions in the room.

B. Answer the questions. Use subject pronouns. Use these prepositional phrases.

at the bedroom door   at the car door
at the kitchen table   at his work table
at the window

1. Where's Frank?
   He's . . . .

2. Where's Mary?
   . . . .

3. Where's Frank?
   . . . .

4. Where's the shoe repairman?

. . . .

5. Where's Mary?

. . . .

Substitute other illustrations. Describe position of people, using '...at _____.'

C. Read the question and short answer. Write a complete negative sentence using 'at' with time.

Example: Does Frank plan to go at 6:00? No, he doesn't.
He doesn't plan to go at 6:00.

1. Does the party begin at 9:00? No, it doesn't.

. . . .

2. Do Frank's friends want to be there at 6:30? No, they don't.

. . . .

3. Does Mary want to go out at 8:00? No, she doesn't.

. . . .

4. Does Frank plan to be home at 8:00? No, he doesn't.

. . . .

IV Pronunciation practice: stress in compound words

A compound word has two or three words together with one special meaning. Loud stress is always on a syllable in the first word.

A. Repeat the words and sentences. Stress the marked syllable in each compound word.

> políceman   fíreman   óffice building
> políce officer   núrse's uniform

1. There's a políceman.
2. There's a políce officer.
3. There's a fíreman.
4. She's wearing a núrse's uniform.
5. It's an óffice building.

B. Repeat these words and sentences from the story.

> bédroom   ármy shoes
> repáirman   ármy uniform

1. He was in the bédroom.
2. He needs his ármy shoes.
3. He's wearing an ármy uniform.
4. He's a repáirman.

V Dramatization

Two men and a woman: make a play from the story. Read the lines for Frank, Mary and the shoe repairman (shoe rep). Or, try it without the book.

FRANK: Where are my army shoes? Do you know, Mary?

MARY: Your what?

FRANK: My army shoes!

MARY: Oh, Frank. Who knows? I certainly don't know. Why do you want them now, after all these years?

FRANK: I want to wear them with my uniform, of course. Look! I'm wearing it—after twenty-eight years! I need my shoes, too. I'm going to see my old army friends tonight, you know. The party's at eight o'clock. I want to wear my uniform.

MARY: Well, Frank, you're getting a little fat! Where was your uniform?

FRANK: It was with some other old clothes. Now I have all these things, but where are my shoes? I need the right shoes. I don't want to wear these.

What's this? Look at this old yellow piece of paper. It was in my pocket.

MARY: Look at the date, Frank. This is from a shoe repairman. This is a ticket for your shoes.

FRANK: Yes, it is! Now I remember. The shoe repairman has the shoes for my uniform. He was going to fix them for me. My shoes are still there!

MARY: They certainly aren't there now. They certainly aren't there after twenty-eight years!

FRANK: I'm going to see the old man. I have some time now. I'm going to get my shoes!

My army job was near here. I never come here now. The buildings are old. It's all very old. Is this the right street? Yes, I think it is. The shoe repairman is a very old man now. Is he still living? Is he still here? He's very old now—and I'm old, too. Twenty-eight years!

SHOE REP: *(Mumbles)*

FRANK: Hello. I think you have my old shoes. You were going to fix them for me. My name is on this ticket.

SHOE REP: Oh, yes, I remember. I have them. They're here. They're in the back room. I repair a lot of army shoes, you know. Yes, yes, here they are.

Yes, I have them. Yes, I'm going to fix them, too. I'm very busy, you know. I repair a lot of army shoes. I'm always busy. I never have enough time. Here are your shoes, but they aren't ready now. Come back next Monday!

READING

may 23rd

Tom Langton has a small food store. He goes to work very early every morning and comes home late at night. He stays at the store for fifteen hours every day. He isn't with his wife for those fifteen hours, and he's glad about that.

He doesn't like to be near his wife. She has trouble with her back. She stays in bed a lot of the time. After three years now, Tom thinks she's never going to get well. He doesn't like his life and he wants to do something about it. "Am I going to take care of Alice all my life? I'm still young. I don't want a sick wife, but who's going to take care of her? I don't know, but I'm not going to do it."

He doesn't love her, but he tries to be nice to her. It's not hard because he has only a little more time with her. He plans to leave. He saves his money. He plans to take his money and leave on the twenty-third of May.

Alice Langton isn't ill now. Her husband thinks she still is, of course. Everybody in town thinks she is. Her back doesn't hurt and she feels well now, but she's lazy.

She stays in bed a lot of the time. She stays in bed and thinks and plans. She's planning to take a trip. She's going to leave her husband and use his money. Alice thinks her husband earns a lot of money. He never gives her much and she thinks he saves his money. She's planning to find the money and take it.

Alice thinks her husband wants to leave her. "He's always nice to me. Why is he nice? He doesn't love me and I know it. He's planning something. I think he's planning to leave me. Well, I'm leaving first, and I'm going to use his money!"

She certainly has no love for Tom.

The days are long for Tom now. It's hard to be nice to the people in the store. He thinks about his plan all the time.

An old man comes into the store every day. He has no money but he wants food from the store. Sometimes Tom gives him something, but today Tom is feeling angry and he isn't nice to the old man.

"Not today! I have enough problems! You're a lazy old man. Why don't you work and buy your food?"

The old man is angry at Tom, but Tom is right. The old man is lazy. He leaves the store and then he starts to laugh.

"Yes, I'm lazy," he thinks. "That's right. I don't work much. Sometimes I do a little work, but I don't like it. That's right, but I need something to eat. I don't like to work." He walks down the street and he's still laughing.

Every night Tom closes the store and puts some of the money

in his pocket. He goes home and sits down with one of his books. He opens it to page one, and puts one piece of the paper money on the page. He puts some of the money on every tenth page. Then he closes the book and puts it back. He has all of his money in five red books.

He's happy about his plan. He's going to work at the store for one more week. On May twenty-third, he's going to take a trip on a plane. He's going to go to Australia and start a new life.

Alice Langton gets up about ten o'clock every morning. She gets something to eat and sometimes she goes back to bed. But now her plan is ready. She has something important to do today. It's time to look for her husband's money. She thinks it's in the house. "He comes home late every night. I know he has money from the store. Where does he put it? I never see him at night because I always go to bed early. I'm going to look for that money in every room and I'm going to find it!"

Alice was up all day that day. She was looking for the money. "Where is it? It's not in any of these rooms. Where is it? I know it's here. I know it!"

She was up all day the next day, too. She was still looking for the money and she was getting tired. She was lazy and looking for the money was a lot of work.

It's May twenty-second and Tom is in his store. Tomorrow is the important day. He's very happy and he's singing and laughing. "Tomorrow... Tomorrow... Tomorrow... No more problems..."

The old man comes into the store again. "Oh, you're here again," Tom said.

"Well, I'm going to try to sell a little trash," said the old man. "Do you have any old clothes or other things at home? Do you have any trash here? Selling trash is a lot of work, but I need a little money."

Tom still doesn't like the old man, but he isn't going to see him again. This is the end of it! "Oh, I think there's some trash at home. There are some old clothes and other things, too. I don't need my old things now. Ask my wife to give them to you."

The old man is glad to get the things from Mrs. Langton. She gives a lot of things to the old man. She's very angry because she still doesn't have the money. She gives a lot of her husband's things to the old man because she's angry.

The old man is happy to have the red books. He likes to read and he's going to sell the books after he reads them. He isn't going to work again for a long, long time.

EXERCISES

I Do you know these words from the story?

sell   lazy   store
everybody   trash

A. Read these sentences:

1. Tom has a food *store*.
   He *sells* many kinds of food.

2. This woman is buying some vegetables, bread and meat.
   She's giving Tom $5.15.
   She's going to take the food home for dinner.

3. Alice is *lazy*.
   She doesn't want to work.
   She doesn't like to work.

4. These things have no use.
   They're *trash*.
   We don't keep them.

B. Use the pronoun 'everybody.'

1. *Everybody* is another word for "all the people."

2. *Everybody* is the subject in these sentences. Look at the verb forms.

> Everybody *is* here on time.
> Everybody *thinks* Alice is sick.
> Everybody *likes* the little girl.

3. Complete these sentences. Use the correct form of these verbs: stay, want, read.

a. Everybody . . . . to go there.
b. Everybody . . . . home on Sunday.
c. Everybody . . . . well.

II What do you remember?

Answer the questions.

1. Is Alice ill now?
2. Who thinks Alice is ill?
3. Is Alice happy?
4. Does Tom think Alice is going to get well?
5. Is Tom nice to his wife?
6. Where does Tom work?
7. Why doesn't Tom come home early?
8. What is Alice's plan?
9. What is Tom's plan?
10. Where does Tom put his money?
11. Does Alice find the money?
12. Does the old man have any food?
13. What does the old man want to sell?
14. What does Alice give the old man?
15. What is the old man going to do with the books?

EXERCISES continued

III Practice with the prepositions 'for,' 'to,' and 'from...to'

A. Complete these sentences using 'for' and these words:

student	table	birthday party
class	child	living room

Example:

The pen is *for the student.*

1. The coat is *for the* . . . .

2. The flowers are *for the* . . . .

3. The books are *for the* . . . .

4. The new rug is *for the* . . . .

5. The cake is *for the* ......

B. Answer these questions about the story. Begin the sentences with 'It's.'
Example:
The story is for the students. Who is it for?
It's for the students.

1. There's some fruit in the refrigerator for Alice. Who is it for?   ....

2. The trash is for the old man. Who is it for?   ....

3. The money is for the trip. What is it for?   ....

4. The food is for her breakfast. What is it for?   ....

5. The money from the store is for Tom. Who is it for?   ....

C. Make 'yes/no' questions using 'to' from these sentences about the story, and answer them with short answers.
Examples:
Alice is going to bed.
Is Alice going to bed?
Yes, she is.

Alice isn't going to bed.
Isn't Alice going to bed?
Yes, she is.

1. Alice is giving things to the old man.

.... ? ....

2. Tom's opening the book to page one.

........................? ....

3. Tom isn't giving much money to Alice.

........................? ....

4. Tom's planning a trip to Australia.

........................? ....

5. Tom isn't giving any food to the old man.

........................? ....

D. Read the sentences using 'from...to' with time. Complete the sentences using 'for.' Use:

for three hours   for fifteen hours
for seven days   for six months
for seven hours

Example:

He studies from three o'clock to six.
He studies *for three hours.*

1. He works from seven o'clock a.m. to ten p.m.

He works ....

2. She looks for the money from ten o'clock to five.

She looks for the money ....

3. He waits from Sunday to Saturday.

He waits ....

4. He plans from January to June.

He plans ....

5. She plans from nine o'clock to noon.

She plans ....

IV The conjunction 'and'

A. Make new sentences using 'and.' Use this example:

Tom's tired.
He wants to go to bed.
Tom's tired and wants to go to bed.

1. Tom goes home.
   He sits down with one of his books.

   . . . .

2. He closes the book.
   He puts it back.

   . . . .

3. Alice stays in bed.
   She plans her trip.

   . . . .

4. He goes to work early.
   He comes home late.

   . . . .

5. Every night Tom closes the store.
   He puts some of the money in his pocket.

   . . . .

6. The old man comes into the store.
   He asks for something to eat.

   . . . .

7. She's angry about the money.
   She gives a lot of things to the old man.

   . . . .

B. Make new sentences using 'and.' Use this example:

> He's singing.
> He's laughing.
> *He's singing and laughing.*

1. Alice's looking for the money.
   She's getting tired.

   . . . .

2. Tom's saving his money.
   He's planning a trip.

   . . . .

3. Tom's talking to the old man.
   He's getting angry.

   . . . .

V The frequency adverbs 'always,' 'never' and 'sometimes'

A. Fill in the correct adverb in these sentences about the story. Use 'always,' 'never' and 'sometimes'

1. Tom . . . . goes to work early in the morning.
2. Does Alice . . . . stay in bed all day? Yes, she does.
3. Tom . . . . gives Alice much money.
4. . . . . Alice goes back to bed in the morning.
5. Tom is . . . . nice to Alice.
6. The old man . . . . likes to work.
7. Tom . . . . closes the store late at night.
8. Alice . . . . wants to work hard.

B. Write these sentences from dictation.

(Use 'always' and 'never' after the verb be, and before other verbs.)

1. Some people are never happy.

2. A few people are always angry.
3. Some people never arrive on time.
4. A lot of people always leave early.

VI Pronunication practice: present tense verbs

Repeat these present tense verbs from the story.

1. *These verbs have an 's' sound at the end.*

thinks	gets	wants
takes	puts	sits
starts	likes	

2. *These verbs have a 'z' sound at the end.*

goes	comes	stays
tries	plans	saves
feels	earns	gives
finds	reads	opens
knows	sells	needs
has		

3. *These verbs have an 'iz' sound at the end.*

uses	closes	fixes

READING

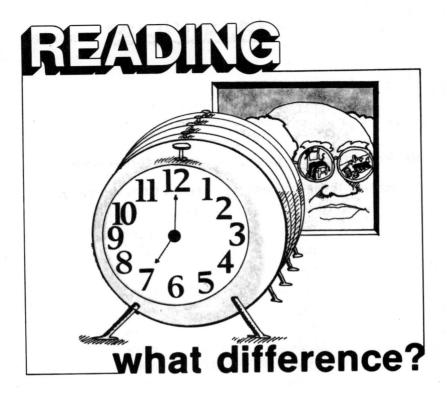

what difference?

It is Friday morning and Mr. Wilson's alarm clock rings. Mr. Wilson opens his eyes and looks at the clock. It is 7:00 a.m. He gets up and walks into the bathroom. He gets up at the same time every day. He does all the same things every day.

Then he stops and thinks, "I'm getting old. My hair isn't black now. I'm getting a little fat, too. Oh, well, who looks at me?"

After he takes a shower, he gets ready for work.

It is 7:40 a.m. and it is time for Mr. Wilson to go to the restaurant for breakfast. He looks at his room. Yesterday's clothes are on a chair. There are a lot of dishes on the table. The room is not clean. "Oh, well," thinks Mr. Wilson. "What difference does it make? Who's going to see it? I have no friends. My life is always the same. Nothing is different. There is never a difference."

The cars are making a lot of noise. There are always a lot of cars and a lot of people. "They're driving too fast. They're walking too fast. Why are they running? Where are they going? I don't like this city. Oh, well, what difference does it make?"

Mr. Wilson opens the door of the restaurant and walks in. He sits down at a table. He always sits at the same table. He has the same breakfast every morning, too. He always has eggs, juice and tea.

Everybody in the restaurant is talking and eating fast. There is a lot of noise. Mr. Wilson doesn't listen. He begins to eat his breakfast.

Then the cook calls, "Fire! Fire! Get the firemen!"

Now there is more noise all around Mr. Wilson. People are running to the door. "Let's go!"

Mr. Wilson doesn't get up. He is sitting at his table in the corner. He doesn't hear the noise and he doesn't know there is a fire!

Firemen run into the restaurant. Newspapermen are there, too. Mr. Wilson sits in the corner and doesn't look up.

Soon the firemen stop the fire. The hungry people come back into the restaurant.

Mr. Wilson finishes his breakfast, puts some money on the table, and walks to the door. He always leaves at the same time.

Mr. Wilson looks up at the tall buildings. "There are too many tall buildings in this city. There are tall buildings on every street. They're all the same."

A small boy is standing on the street. He has some

newspapers.

"Is there any good news in the newspaper today?" Mr. Wilson asks the boy.

"Oh, yes, It's a big world. There's always good news. Are you going to buy a paper?"

"All right. Here's the money."

Mr. Wilson walks to the corner. The bus comes at the same time every day, and Mr. Wilson always sits down in the same seat and reads the newspaper. He likes to read all the stories about the good things and the bad things in the world—the good people and the bad people. "At least they aren't all the same," he thinks.

There are a lot of people on the bus and there is a lot of noise.

Mr. Wilson doesn't look at the people and he doesn't hear the noise.

Then a man on the bus calls, "Look! That car is going to hit our bus!"

The car doesn't hit the bus, but it hits another car. The bus stops and everybody looks at the accident. People run from the buildings to look at the accident. Soon, two police cars are there.

There is a lot of noise, but Mr. Wilson doesn't look up. He doesn't know about the accident. The bus starts again and soon Mr. Wilson gets up from his seat. His office is in the bank on the next corner.

He is on time for work. He's always on time. He goes to his desk, sits down and starts to work. The long day at the bank begins.

He doesn't like his job. "It isn't a very interesting job. Every day is the same, but at least there isn't any noise here. I don't like noise."

At 11:00, Mr. Wilson stands up. "I think I'm going to have some tea." He looks around and sees a tall man coming in the door. The man is wearing black clothes and a black hat.

"Well, he seems interesting," Mr. Wilson thinks, "He's tall and he's wearing those black clothes. It's interesting to be so tall."

26 what difference?

Mr. Wilson goes to get his tea. He always has some tea at this time.

The tall man goes to the teller window. He gives a piece of paper to the man at the teller window. The piece of paper says:

'This is a robbery.
Give me all the money.
Don't call for help.'

The man at the window is looking at the robber. "What am I going to do?" he's thinking. Then he gives the tall man all the money. The robber puts it in his pocket and runs.

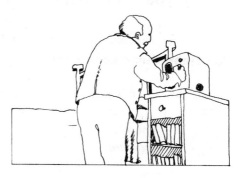

"Stop! Stop! Help! It's a robbery!"

The bank policemen run after the tall man. There's a lot of noise in the bank. More policemen arrive.

In another room, Mr. Wilson is drinking his tea, and he doesn't hear any noise.

He's thinking, "Tomorrow, I'm not going to get up early. There's nothing interesting to do." He goes back to his desk. There isn't any noise in the bank now.

He finishes his work at 5:00. It's time to go home.

Mr. Wilson's day wasn't interesting. It was like all his days.

He's getting ready to go to bed and he's listening to the radio.

"Today there was a fire in a restaurant, a car accident, and a bank robbery!"

Mr. Wilson is tired. "I never see interesting things."

EXERCISES

I   Do you know these words from the story?

hit   bank   robber   same
accident   teller   noise   different

A.   Read these sentences.

1. One car is going to *hit* the other car.
    There's going to be an *accident*.

2. The big boy is hitting the little boy.
    This is not an accident.
    He's angry and he wants to hurt the little boy.

3. He's hitting the ball.
    He's having a good time.

4. Mr. Wilson works in a *bank*.
    He works in the banking business.
    It's good to keep your money in a bank.

5. A *teller* is a bank worker.
    He works with a lot of money every day.

6. In the story, the tall man takes money from the bank.
    It isn't his money, but he wants it and he takes it.
    He's a *robber,* and he's robbing the bank.
    It's a bank robbery.

7. She's making a *noise*.
   She's making a lot of noise.

8. He isn't making any noise.

9. These are the *same*.
   There is no difference.

10. These are *different*.
    There is a difference.

B. Complete the words in these sentences.

1. There wasn't any n_____.
2. The man was calling, "It's a r_____!"
3. It's always the same. There's no d_____.
4. Mr. Wilson has a job in a ____.
5. Is today going to be _____?
6. The t_____ gives the r_____ the money in this story.
7. Mr. Wilson's days are all the ____.
8. Sometimes people are hurt in _____.

EXERCISES continued

II What do you remember?
Answer the questions:

1. What time does Mr. Wilson get up?
2. What does he look like?
3. Is Mr. Wilson's room clean?
4. How does it look?
5. What does Mr. Wilson always have for breakfast?
6. Who calls, "Fire! Fire!"?
7. When does Mr. Wilson leave the restaurant?
8. What does he do on the bus?
9. Tell about the accident.
10. What's a robber?
11. What does the robber look like?
12. Did Mr. Wilson see the robbery?
13. What does Mr. Wilson hear on the radio?
14. Did he have an interesting day?

III Practice with the prepositions 'in' and 'at'

A. Repeat these sentences using 'in.'
Example:

The bed's in the bédroom.

1. He's in his cár.
2. She's in the building.
3. It's in his pócket.
4. She's in the kítchen.
5. They're in the hóuse.
6. Mr. Wilson's in his óffice.

7. He's in a réstaurant.

8. His office is in a bánk.

9. There's wáter in the bottle.

10. There's téa in the glass.

11. There's mílk in the glass.

12. There's nóthing in the glass.

13. There's nóthing in the bottle.

14. There's a róbber in the bank.

15. There's a mán in the building.

16. There's a fíre in the restaurant.

Repeat the sentences. Use the past form.

B. Read the sentences using 'in' with time. Complete the sentences using 'at.'

Example:

I'm leaving in a minute. I'm leaving *at 9:30.*

It's 9:29.

1. He's leaving in a minute. He's leaving . . . .

It's 12:29.

2. He's leaving in a few minutes. He's leaving . . . .

3. She's coming in an hour. She's
   coming ....

4. The class begins in an hour and a
   half. The class begins ....

5. We're having lunch in two and a
   half hours. We're having lunch
   ....

6. We're going in a quarter of an
   hour. We're going ....

IV The conjunction 'and'

A. Make new sentences using 'and.' Use this example:

Mr. Wilson opens his eyes.
He looks at the clock.
Mr. Wilson opens his eyes and looks at the clock.

1. He gets up.
   He walks into the bathroom.

   ....

2. Then he stops.
   He thinks, "I'm getting old."

   ....

3. Mr. Wilson opens the door of the restaurant.
   He walks in.

   . . . .

4. He sits in the corner.
   He doesn't look up.

   . . . .

5. He always sits down in the same seat.
   He reads the newspaper.

   . . . .

6. He puts some money on the table.
   He walks to the door.

   . . . .

7. The robber goes to the man at the window.
   He gives him a piece of paper.

   . . . .

B. Make a new sentence using 'and.' Use this example:

He goes to his desk.
He sits down.
He starts to work.
He goes to his desk, sits down and starts to work.

1. Mr. Wilson leaves his desk.
   He goes to another room.
   He gets a cup of tea.

   . . . .

2. The robber gives him a piece of paper.
   He takes the money.
   He runs.

   . . . .

3. Mr. Wilson gets ready for bed.
   He turns on the radio.
   He listens to it.

   . . . .

V   The determiners 'a,' 'the,' 'a lot of,' 'a little,' 'some' and 'any'

A. Complete these sentences. Use:

a lot of   a little   some   any

1. It's making . . . . noise.

2. It isn't making . . . . noise.

3. He's making . . . . noise.
4. He's only making . . . . . . noise.

5. They're making . . . . noise.

6. They aren't making .... noise.

B. Complete these sentences. Use:

the same	different
a difference	no difference

1. These are *the same.*
   There is *no difference.*

2. These are *different.*
   There is *a difference.*

3. These are . . . .
   There is . . . .

4. These are . . . .
   There is . . . .

5. These are . . . .
   There is . . . .

6. These are . . . .
   There is . . . .

C. Write these sentences from dictation:

1. His days were all the same.
2. There was never a difference.
3. One day was different.
4. What was the difference?

VI Uses of the present tense

A. Study these uses of the present tense.

1. We use the present tense with *every* day/morning, etc.
   I get up early every morning.

2. We use the present tense with *always, never,* and *sometimes.*

The earth always moves around the sun.

The sun never moves around the earth.

These sentences are always true.

My class always begins at 9:00.

I never walk to that restaurant.

Sometimes I go to see a play.

These sentences are always true for the speaker.

3. Sometimes we write stories in the present tense.

John's very tired. He walks to the chair. He sits down and drinks a glass of water.

These sentences describe (tell about) this man on one day. They are not true every day. They are not always true.

We don't use this form much in conversation.

4. We write play directions in the present tense.

B. Perform this play

This little play is a pantomime play (the people in the play do not speak). It is from the story, "What Difference?"

Student A: The Director   *Read the directions*

Student B: Mr. Wilson   *Listen to the*
Student C: The man at the bank window   *Director. Do*
Student D: The bank robber   *your part. Do*
Student E: A policeman   *not speak.*

WHAT'S THE DIFFERENCE?

Directions for the people in the play. The Director reads them aloud.

Mr. Wilson is at his desk.

He gets up from his desk.

He goes to another room to get some tea.

The bank robber comes into the bank.

He walks to the man at the teller window.

He gives a piece of paper to the man at the window.

The man at the window reads the piece of paper.

He thinks, "What am I going to do?"

He gives the robber all the money.

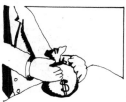

The robber leaves the bank.

The teller runs to get the policeman.

The policeman runs after the bank robber.

Mr. Wilson comes into the room.
He sits down at his desk.
He doesn't know about the robbery.
He thinks, "There's nothing interesting in this bank."

READING

the beautiful spy

Certainly all the important people in Washington remember Mrs. Rose Greenhow. She was my good friend and, of course, I remember her very well. I'm getting old now, and this is an old story, but I want to tell you about her.

How do I tell her story? How does it begin? I suppose it begins at one of her famous dinner parties in 1862. During the Civil War, men from the North and the South knew and loved this beautiful young woman. She had no husband then, and she enjoyed having parties.

The army of the North was fighting the army of the South. Sometimes brothers were fighting brothers. It was a very difficult time for all of us. Many important men from the government of the North came to parties at Mrs. Greenhow's home.

One night, some of them came—to forget the war and have a

good time. And they did! They enjoyed her dinner of duck and vegetables and a big white cake. During their dinner, they talked about their plans for fighting the army of the South. Mrs. Greenhow listened.

She listened because she had a plan, too. These men didn't know it, but Mrs. Greenhow was not their friend and she was no friend of the North. This beautiful young woman was a spy!

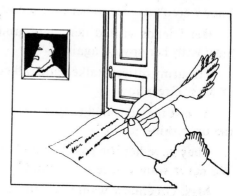

Mrs. Greenhow didn't eat very much. She was thinking about her plan. She was going to write a letter to the army officers of the South. She was going to tell them all about this dinner party.

At last it was time for dessert. The men were eating their cake and Mrs. Greenhow went into another room. She was there for about fifteen minutes, but the men were having a good time. It was all right.

She wrote the important letter and gave it to her maid. The maid took it to another friend of the South. "I know my letter is going to help the South," Mrs. Greenhow said. She was happy.

She went back to the dinner table. Soon she and all the men were laughing and singing.

Mrs. Greenhow's famous parties were always like that. All the men had a good time and they talked a lot. Mrs. Greenhow listened.

Then, one day, an officer of the North asked a few questions about her. Soon he knew a lot about the beautiful young spy, and Mrs. Greenhow was in trouble. But the army officers had a problem. What were they going to do with a woman spy?

They decided to keep her in her house for a few months. "That's going to be enough to stop her," they thought.

But it wasn't enough. Soon Mrs. Greenhow knew more about the North's plans. She told the South. Her maid helped her and a lot of other people did, too. By this time she was very important to the South, but the North learned of her spying a second time. They weren't so nice to her the second time. She went to prison.

Her friends visited her there, and believe it or not, she was busy with her spying again!

The army officers talked and talked about the serious problem of Mrs. Greenhow.

At last they decided to give her a passport to the South. "It's the only thing to do."

They gave her the passport and they said, "Don't come back! We never want to see you again!"

Mrs. Greenhow wanted no more trouble with the North. She went to a city in the South and waited. She waited and waited, but the men were still fighting.

The South was having a difficult time. There wasn't enough money. They needed more money. Mrs. Greenhow and six important men of the South decided to go to England. They were going to try to get some gold from the English.

They traveled by ship, of course, and it was a very long trip back, but they had the gold!

"We have only one more day on this ship, and I'm so glad," said Mrs. Greenhow. "It was a very long trip and our people need the gold. They need so many things."

The next morning it started to rain hard. The weather was very bad. The workers were having trouble with the ship.

In the evening, one of Mrs. Greenhow's friends called, "Land!

Land! I see land! Oh, but look at it! Where are we?"

Mrs. Greenhow and the other five men looked. "I know," said one of them. "We're in the North, and we certainly don't want to be here. We don't want their men to see us on this ship."

"They're going to get us and the gold, too," said another man.

"No! No! The money is for the South," cried Mrs. Greenhow. "What are we going to do?"

"Let's not stay on the ship," said the first man. "Let's use a small boat. There's one over there. The weather is still bad. Let's use that boat, then buy some horses, and ride back to the South. It's the only thing to do."

"What about the money?" asked another man. "Where are we going to put it? It's not paper money, you know. It's gold and it's heavy. I don't want to take all of it. Let's only take a little of it. You know the North's army is on that land. I don't want the North to get our gold and I don't want to go to prison. Let's take only a little of the money to buy the horses. Please listen to me!"

"No! The money is important," said Mrs. Greenhow. "Listen to me! I have a plan. I'm going to put the gold under my clothes. We're going to take all of it to the South!"

Soon the six men and Mrs. Greenhow were ready to go. It was still raining.

The little boat was full and the weather was bad. After about ten minutes, the boat started to go down!

"Swim! Swim! Look! There's the land!" called one of the men.

Mrs. Greenhow had the heavy pieces of gold under her clothes. She was trying to swim, but it was very hard. "The South needs the gold. The gold is so heavy..."

The six men were on land. They waited for Mrs. Greenhow, but she didn't come. They looked for her, but there was only the angry black sea.

EXERCISES

I   Do you know these words from the story?

Civil War   spy   boat
the North   prison   gold
the South   ship

A.   Read these sentences:

1. A war between people of the same country is a *Civil War*.
   There was a Civil War in the United States from 1861 to 1865.
   The people of *the North* were fighting the people of *the South*.

2. In this story about the Civil War, Mrs. Greenhow is a *spy*.
   She wants the South to win the war.
   She learns about the plans of the Northern army.
   Then she tells her friends in the South.

3. A Northern officer knows about her spying.
   The Northern army puts her in *prison*.

4. Mrs. Greenhow went to England in a *ship* like this.

A modern ship

A little *boat*

5. *Gold* is a yellow metal.

We use gold for money.

People make and use pretty things of gold.

B. Complete the new words and review verbs from the story.

1. Mrs. Greenhow w_____ a letter and g___ it to her maid.
2. Her maid t____ the letter to a friend of the S_____.

3. One officer k____ Mrs. Greenhow was a ___ .
4. They took a long trip on a big ____,
   not on a little ____.
5. There are many kinds of p_____s.
6. There was a C____ ___ in the United
   States from 1861 to 1865.

II What do you remember?

Answer the questions.

1. Why did the men go to Mrs. Greenhow's party on a night during the war?
2. What kind of meat did Mrs. Greenhow serve for dinner?
3. What was Mrs. Greenhow's plan on the night of the party?
4. Why did she have parties for the men of the North?
5. Who took the letter for the spy?
6. How many people went to England? Who were they? Why did they go?
7. What was the plan for going back to the South after they saw land?
8. Who took the gold? How?
9. Why did they leave the ship?

III Practice with the preposition 'of'

A. Complete these sentences. (Use 'the' = 'the only one.')

Example:

The chair has a back.
   This is *the back of the chair.*
   How many *backs does it have?*
   It *has one back.*

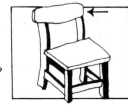

1. The chair has a seat.
    This is ....

    How many .... ?
    It ....

2. The room has a floor.
    This is ....

    How many .... ?
    It ....

3. The pen has a point.
    This is ....

    How many .... ?
    It ....

B. Complete these sentences. (Use 'a' = 'one of several.')
Example:

The chair has four legs.
    This is *a leg of the chair*.
    How many *legs does it have?*
    It *has four legs*.

1. The room has three windows.
    This is ....
    How many .... ?
    It ....

2. The room has four walls.

   This is ....

   How many .... ?

   It ....

3. The newspaper has many pages.

   This is ....

   How many .... ?

   It ....

C. Write these sentences again. Use 'of.'

   Example:

   The North's army was on the land.
   The army of the North was on the land.

1. The South's army was hungry.

   ....

2. The ship's officers were having trouble, too.

   ....

3. The spy's friends were officers.

   ....

4. The North's famous prisoner was Mrs. Greenhow.

   ....

5. The country's people were fighting.

   ....

D. Write these sentences again. Use 'It's.'

   Example: This is the tenth of September.
   It's September 10th.

1. This is the second of February. ....

2. This is the thirty-first of March. ....

3. This is the seventh of July. ....

4. This is the first of May. ....

IV The conjunction 'and'

A. Make a new sentence using 'and.' Omit subject noun after 'and.'

Example:

Many men knew her.

Many men loved her.

Many men knew her and loved her.

1. The men laughed.

The men had a good time.

....

2. She wrote a letter.

She gave it to her maid.

....

3. He asked a lot of questions.

He learned a lot about the spy.

....

4. They gave her a passport.

They said, "Don't come back!"

....

5. She went to a city in the South.

She waited and waited.

....

B. Make a new sentence using 'and.' Omit 'let's' after 'and.'

Example:

> Let's use the money to buy some horses.
> Let's ride back to the South.
>
> *Let's use the money to buy some horses and ride back to the South.*

1. Let's have dinner together.
    Let's talk about our plans.

    . . . .

2. Let's stop Mrs. Greenhow's spying.
    Let's put her in prison.

    . . . .

3. Let's take only a little of the money.
    Let's leave in that small boat.

    . . . .

V Pronunciation practice

A. Repeat these past verb forms from the story.

1. These verbs have a '*d*' sound at the end.

loved	enjoyed
listened	traveled
called	cried
learned	

2. These verbs have a '*t*' sound at the end.

talked	asked
helped	looked

3. These verbs have an '*id*' sound at the end.

decided	visited
wanted	waited
needed	started

B. **Write and repeat the base form of these irregular verbs.**
   Example:

   | ate | *eat* |
   | got | *get* |

1. knew ....
2. had ....
3. came ....
4. did ....
5. went ....
6. wrote ....
7. gave ....
8. took ....
9. thought ....

C. **Write these sentences from dictation.**

1. The officers laughed and talked.
2. She listened and learned.
3. She waited a while and started again.
4. They knew she went back to the South.

READING

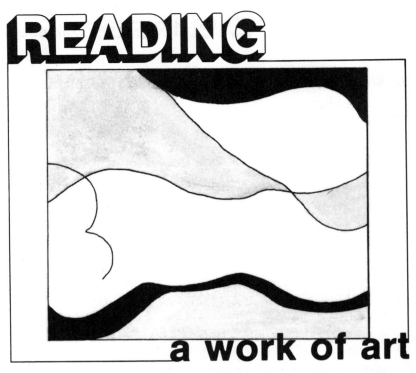

a work of art

adapted from the story by Anton Chekhov

Sasha Smirnov, the only son of his mother, walked into the office of Doctor Koshelkov. Sasha had something under his arm.

"Well, my boy," said the doctor to his young friend. "How are you feeling today? Not sick now, are you?"

"No, Doctor. I am well!"

"That's good. You seem happy. Why are you here?" asked the doctor.

Sasha put his hand over his heart and said, "My mother wants me to thank you. I'm my mother's only son. She thought I was never going to get well, but I did. You took very good care of me."

"Oh, Sasha. I'm glad to see you well and happy. I need no thanks."

"I am the only son of my mother. I have no father. We have no money to give you for your help, but my mother and I want you to take this gift. It's a wonderful work of art. It's very old and very beautiful."

The doctor said, "No, no. This isn't necessary. I don't need this at all."

"Please take it," said Sasha.

The doctor took the gift from Sasha, and began to open it. It had newspapers and string around it, and he had some trouble with the string. While he was opening it, Sasha said, "My mother and I want you to have this because we love it. It was my father's."

Sasha picked up the newspapers and the doctor put the work of art on the table. It was a statue of two women. They had no clothes and they were...

The doctor looked at the statue and then he looked at Sasha. He looked down and put his hand over his eyes. He was thinking, "What a statue! What am I going to say to Sasha?"

When he looked up, Sasha was laughing and saying, "Are you happy? Isn't it wonderful?"

"Yes, it's pretty," the doctor said, "but it isn't very..."

"Isn't very what?" asked Sasha.

"Well, it's... I think it's a... a bad thing to have in my house."

"What ideas you have!" Sasha said. "It's very beautiful. Look at it! It's a beautiful work of art. I look at it and I want to cry."

"Yes, yes, I know," said the doctor, "but I have a wife and children. The children come often into this room. I don't want them to see this."

Sasha said, "Of course, some people don't understand art, but I know you do. You had a good education and you are an important man. We knew it was a good gift for you. There are only two statues in the world like this, but we don't have the other one now. The two statues are beautiful together."

"That's all right, Sasha. That's all right. One is enough. Where am I going to put it? The children come in here, you know. Do you understand?"

Sasha didn't understand. "Put it there on your desk," he said.

"I don't know," said the doctor. "I don't know. Well, thank you. I certainly don't want to argue with you. Thank you, thank you."

While he was standing there looking at the statue, Sasha went home to tell his mother about the doctor and the gift.

"It's a beautiful thing, I suppose," thought the doctor. "My wife isn't going to like it and she isn't going to want me to keep it here. I don't want her to see it!"

He sat down and thought about it. "I have an idea. I'm going to give the statue to my good old friend, Ukhov. Children don't go in lawyer's offices, and he doesn't have a wife." He laughed and looked at the statue again. "I think he's going to like this terrible statue."

The doctor took the statue to Ukhov's office.

"Good morning, my friend," he said. "I came here to thank you."

"To thank me for what?" asked Ukhov.

"Remember the work you did for me? You didn't take my money because we're friends, but I brought you a gift. This is a beautiful work of art."

"Yes, it is a beautiful thing. Where did you get it?" asked Ukhov. He didn't wait for the doctor's answer. He said, "I don't want to take it, old friend. Please keep it."

"Why?" asked Doctor Koshelkov.

"Sometimes women come to my office!" answered Ukhov. "And I don't want to take it home because my mother often visits me at home."

"Don't say another word," laughed the doctor. "I know you're going to enjoy it. I'm going back to my office now. I'm very busy. Goodbye!"

The lawyer looked at the statue. "It is a beautiful thing, but what am I going to do with it?"

He thought about it all day. In the evening, he went to see his friend, Shoshkin. He took the statue with him. He went to the theater because Shoshkin was acting in a play.

Ukhov looked for Shoshkin, but he wasn't in his room. Ukhov wrote a letter and put it on a table with the statue. "Shoshkin likes to act, and he likes works of art. This is a good gift for him," thought Ukhov.

After the play, Shoshkin's friends came to his room to see him. They laughed and talked about the statue.

"What am I going to do with this beautiful work of art?" laughed Shoshkin.

"Why don't you want it?" asked his friend and he was laughing, too.

"Oh, it's terrible!" said Shoshkin, and he picked up the statue. "Here! I'm giving it to you."

"No, no, I don't want it," said his friend. "Wait a minute! I know an old woman. She loves things like this. I'm going to take it to her and get some money for it!"

Shoshkin went with his friend to see the old woman. She was Mrs. Smirnov.

The next day, Doctor Koshelkov was working at his desk when Sasha came again. He had something under his arm.

"Doctor, look! I have good news!" Sasha said. "I'm so happy and my mother is, too. Now we have the other statue! We want to thank you again, and we're giving this statue to you, too! A man came to see my mother last night, and he had it! Here it is! Now you have the two statues!" He put it on the desk.

The doctor opened his mouth to say something, but Sasha didn't hear a word! And that was a good thing!

EXERCISES

I Do you know these words from the story?

work of art   statue   gift

A. Read these sentences:

1. Artists make things with their hands.

Some artists paint pictures.

Some artists make *statues*.

Artists make many different kinds of beautiful things.

2. A beautiful painting or statue is a *work of art*.

3. People give nice things to their friends or family on important days.
    They give *gifts* because they love their friends and family.
    Birthdays are important days for giving gifts in many countries.

4. Sometimes people give gifts to other people to say "Thank you."
    Sasha's gift for the doctor was a "thank you" gift.

B. **Review and write the past form of these verbs.**

1. walk . . . .
2. put   . . . .
3. begin . . . .
4. pick up . . . .
5. sit down . . . .
6. laugh . . . .

II What do you remember?

Put a 'T' in front of the true sentences.
Put an 'F' in front of the false sentences.

. . . . 1. Sasha was his mother's only son.

. . . . 2. Sasha's family had a lot of money.

. . . . 3. Sasha's mother didn't like the statue.

. . . . 4. Sasha was only a boy, but he loved the work of art.

. . . . 5. Doctor Koshelkov was very happy to have the statue.

. . . . 6. Doctor Koshelkov did not have a good education.

. . . . 7. Doctor Koshelkov didn't want his wife to see the statue.

. . . . 8. Ukhov was a doctor, too.

. . . . 9. Ukhov took no money from Doctor Koshelkov.

. . . 10. Sometimes women come to Ukhov's office.

. . . 11. Ukhov liked the statue, but he didn't want to keep it.

. . . 12. Shoshkin thought the statue was beautiful.

. . . 13. Shoshkin went to see Mrs. Smirnov.

. . . 14. Doctor Koshelkov had two statues.

EXERCISES continued

III Practice with the prepositions 'on' and 'off'

A. Action Drill

| Student A | *(doesn't look at Student B* | Put your book on your desk. |

Student B *(does it)*
Student A Did you put it there?
Student B Yes, I did. It's there now.

Student A Put your paper on your book.

Student B *(does it)*
Student A Did you put it there?
Student B Yes, I did. It's there now.

Student A Put your pencil on the teacher's desk.

Student B *(does it)*
Student A Did you put it there?
Student B Yes, I did. It's there now.

Student A Put a picture on the wall.
Student B *(does it)*
Student A Did you put it there?

Student B Yes, I did. It's there now.

Continue by substituting other objects.

B. Write complete sentences. Use: 'Take...off....'

Example:

The book is on the table.
  Take the book off the table, please.

1. Sasha's gift is on the table.

. . . .

2. The newspapers and string are on the chair.

. . . .

3. The statue is on the desk.

. . . .

4. The lawyer's letter is on the table.

. . . .

Repeat the sentences, substituting 'it' or 'them' for the subject noun.

Example:

> The book is on the table.
> *Take it off the table, please.*

IV Verb tense with subordinate clauses (subordinators: 'when,' 'while')

Fill in the right form of the verb in these sentences about the story. Use the verbs in the list.

work	laugh	act
arrive	come	ask
tell	open	stand
put	think	go

Example:

> While the doctor was *opening* the gift, Sasha *told* him more about it.

1. The doctor was . . . ., "What a statue!" when he . . . . his hand over his eyes.

2. While the doctor was . . . . there looking at the statue, Sasha . . . . home.

3. When Ukhov .... at the theater, Shoshkin was .... in a play.

4. Shoshkin's friend was .... when he ...., "Why don't you want it?"

5. When Sasha .... the next day, the doctor was .... at his desk.

V   Appositives

A.   Fill in the right name. Use the names in the list.

> Mrs. Smirnov   Sasha   Ukhov
> Shoshkin   Koshelkov

1. ...., the only son, and his mother were glad.

2. The boy gave the gift to ...., the doctor.

3. ...., the old woman, loved works of art.

4. The doctor gave the gift to ...., the lawyer.

5. Ukhov's friend, ..., was acting in a play.

B.   Write these sentences from dictation.

1. The woman's husband, John, was a tall man.

2. He took the plans to Mr. Smith, the engineer.

3. Do you know Miss Jones, his secretary?

4. Our friends, Jim and Jane, were at the theater.

READING

the whistler

PART I

Vincent Cassidy was the first son in a family with eleven children. Their mother and father gave them a lot of love, but there wasn't much money. They had no money to buy things to play with. The children looked for things to play with in the street and in the park. They played games with other children and whistled at the dogs. Vince learned to be a very good whistler. The family had very little money but they had a lot of fun.

One day, Mr. Cassidy went to bed because he was sick. He didn't get well. He never got up.

Then difficult days began for Mrs. Cassidy and the eleven children. Vince was only thirteen but he was the man of the house. It was necessary for him to leave school and look for a job. The family had no money. It was the only thing to do.

"I'm going down to the dock to look for a job," he said. "I know something about ships because Dad worked there."

Vince got a job. He was only thirteen but he was a big boy. He worked hard for many long hours every day. Day after day he helped get the big ships ready to go. One after the other, the beautiful big ships went to sea, and Vince always waited on the dock to see them go.

The boy was happy when he took his money home to his mother, but it was never enough. They never had enough money for food and clothes. Then his little sister got sick and there wasn't enough money for expensive medicine.

There were no more happy days for Vince. He always felt angry. He was angry at his family and his friends. He was angry at the city and at the dock and at everything he knew. He tried and tried to think of something to do about it.

He talked with the men at the dock. Some of them traveled on the ships. Their work was hard and they didn't like being on the ships in bad weather. But they got more money. And they got some of the money before the ship started every trip!

Vince thought about it for a few days. "What is my life? It's nothing! What do I know about the world? Nothing! I work every day and I work hard but it's never enough. And I don't know how to do any other job. What am I going to do? Well, now I know! I'm going to leave this city and I'm going to earn more money and I'm going to have a good time!"

Vince's mother didn't want him to go, of course, but the ship's officers were glad to have him. Vince was glad because at last he was leaving and he was going to see the world!

PART II

The first few days on the ship were interesting. After that, Vince knew he didn't like being on a ship. He looked at the water and thought about his mother. He looked at the clouds and thought about his sisters and brothers. He certainly wasn't happy.

The ship went to many countries from the north of Europe to

the south. While the ship's officers were busy buying and selling cargo, Vince and the other men enjoyed their short visits in those countries. They listened to people speaking different languages. They looked at people wearing different clothes. Vince learned something about the world. His days weren't very happy but they were interesting.

There was a Civil War in one country. When they came to it, the ship's officers decided not to go in to the dock. But some of the men decided to take small boats and try to find out the news. Vince wanted to go, and he was glad when the ship's officers said yes. Vince was big and the officers forgot he was only fifteen.

The small boats came up to the dock. There were a lot of men wearing army uniforms on the dock, but not many other people. The army officers were angry because the ship didn't come up to the dock, but they didn't stop Vince or his friends. Vince thought they wanted the ship's cargo.

The men walked around the streets for a few hours, but they didn't like being there. They were going to go back to their small boats when three army officers stopped them. The officers took the men to a small building.

The officers took the clothes from Vince and his friends and put the men in small rooms in the building.

There was a window in Vince's little room. He went to the window. There were the officers! They were wearing Vince's clothes and his friends' clothes, and they were taking the small boats. "They're going to the ship! I was sure they wanted the cargo! Now we're in trouble!"

Soon the small boats were near the ship. What were those men going to do? The minutes were like hours. Then the small boats came back! The big ship was leaving!

"They're leaving!" Vince was still standing at the window and he felt a little sick. He didn't want to believe it. "I'm in prison in a foreign country. How long am I going to be here? What about my family? They need me!"

Vince was in prison for two months. The army officers asked him questions every day. "Where did the ship go? Where did they take the cargo? Is the ship coming back?" Vince knew nothing. They gave him a lot of work to do, but they didn't hurt him.

A young girl cooked the food for the prisoners. The food was different. Vince learned to like it. Vince liked the girl, but she didn't want to talk to him. That was all right because their languages were different. After a few weeks, she looked at him, and Vince knew that she liked him, too. They learned to talk a little. They used words from the two languages.

Vince thought about taking her back home with him, but he had no money. He certainly wasn't earning any money in prison! And what ship was going to take him home? And when? "Well," he thought, "I'm going to come back and get her." One day he told her his plan, but she only cried.

"No, no, never, never!" she said again and again. They talked about it many times but she always cried. She always said no.

At last the ship came back for the prisoners. This time, the ship had no cargo, but there were about a hundred more men. The ship came in to the dock. Vince was at his window again.

The ship's officers were talking with the army officers. Some of the other men from the ship ran up the street. They were looking for the prison. Vince saw them and called, "Here! Over here! We're over here!"

There were a few army officers at the prison, but they didn't fight.

Soon, Vince and his friends were running back to the ship. Vince felt wonderful. Then he remembered the girl! He didn't have time to say goodbye to the girl.

The ship was going home. Vince wanted to see his mother and brothers and sisters very much, but he thought about the girl a lot, too. Was he going to see her again? She didn't want to leave her country, but he knew he didn't want to live there! And he didn't want another trip on a ship! He was a land man and now he knew it!

Only a few more hours...

There it was! The dock and the buildings—and his mother was there, too! He was home!

Vince went back to work at the dock. It was still the only thing he knew how to do. This time he worked on the big crane. The long arm of the crane picked up cargo on the dock and put it on the ships.

One of the crane man's helpers had an interesting job. He was the signalman. He whistled signals. He also made signals with his hands and arms. The crane man's eyes stayed on the signalman. The long arm of the crane picked up the right pieces of cargo. The signalman whistled another signal. The arm of the crane put the cargo on the ship. The crane man's eyes stayed on the signalman. There was a lot of noise on the dock. There were a lot of people. The crane man only listened to the signalman's whistle.

Vince was always a good whistler. Now he practiced every day for many weeks. He learned the whistle signals. He learned the hand and arm signals. He got the job and more money. But there was never enough money to save. Sometimes the family needed medicine. Sometimes Vince bought gifts. Still, he always thought about the girl. "One day I'm going to ask her to come!"

Vince liked his job. The months passed. The years passed. His brothers and sisters were men and women and they had children.

Many more years passed and the old man often stopped and looked at the sea when he walked home. "Yes," he said, "it takes a long time to learn to whistle signals well. It's an important job. The crane man needs me down at the dock." Then the old man looked at the sea again and thought about the young girl. "I always wanted to ask her to come."

EXERCISES

I Do you know these words from the story?

cargo   whistle   dock

crane   signal   sea

The *cargo* is on the *dock*.

The signalman *whistles* a *signal* to the crane man.

The arm of the *crane* picks up the cargo and puts it on a ship.

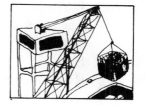

The ship starts its trip at *sea*.

EXERCISES continued

II What do you remember?

Answer the questions.

PART 1

1. How much money did Vince's family have?
2. Did Vince's father get well?
3. When did Vince leave school? Why?
4. Where did Vince get a job?
5. What did his sister need?
6. Was Vince happy about his life and work?

PART 2

7. Where did the ship travel?
8. What did Vince do while the ship's officers were busy?
9. What is a Civil War?
10. Who was on the dock when the small boats came?
11. Why did Vince think the army officers on the dock were angry?
12. Where did the officers take Vince and his friends?
13. Where were Vince's clothes?
14. What do you think the army officers were going to do when they came to the big ship?
15. What did Vince do every day in the prison?
16. How did Vince and the girl talk together?
17. How did Vince leave the prison?

PART 3

18. Where did Vince work after his trip?
19. What is a crane?
20. What does a signalman do?
21. How did Vince use his money?
22. Was Vince a happy man at the end of the story?

III Practice with the prepositions 'into' and 'in'

A. Read these sentences:

1. Mary is pouring the tea into the bottle.

2. Now the tea is in the bottle.

3. Mary is pouring the milk into the glass.

4. The milk is in the glass now.

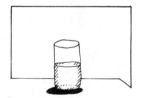

5. Mary is putting the bottle into the refrigerator.

6. The bottle is in the refrigerator now.

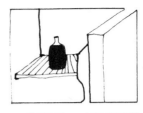

7. John is putting the money into his wallet.

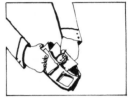

8. Now the money is in the wallet.

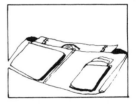

B. Repeat the sentences in Part A. Substitute one of the following words for 'the milk,' 'the tea,' etc.

it   some   a little

Example:

Mary is pouring *it* into the bottle.

Mary is pouring *some* into the bottle.

Mary is pouring *a little* into the bottle.

C. Fill in the right preposition. Use 'into' or 'in.'

1. Vince went *into* his father's room.

His father was *in* bed.

2. Vince went .... the office.

The officers were .... their office.

3. The officers took him .... a little room.

He was .... the room for two months.

4. The girl took the food .... the prison.

Vince ate .... his little room.

5. He went .... the store.

He bought gifts .... the store.

6. He went .... his house.

He sat .... his chair and thought about the girl.

IV Questions with 'did,' 'was,' 'were' and short answers

Write short answers to these questions.

Example:

Was Vince a good whistler? *Yes, he was.*

1. Did Mr. Cassidy get sick?   ....

2. Was Vince fifteen when he went to work?   ....

3. Was Vince happy about his job?   ....

4. Did Vince want to have a good time?   ....

5. Did the men enjoy visiting other countries?   ....

6. Did the ship go to the dock in every country?   ....

7. Was there a Civil War in one country?   ....

8. Did the ship's officers let Vince go to the dock on the small boat?   . . . .

9. Were the army officers on the dock happy?   . . . .

10. Did the girl speak Vince's language?   . . . .

11. Did the big ship come back for the prisoners?   . . . .

12. Did Vince want another trip on a ship?   . . . .

13. Was the signalman's job interesting?   . . . .

14. Did Vince practice the signals?   . . . .

15. Did Vince think his job was important?   . . . .

V Subordinate clauses (subordinators 'when' and 'while')

Write these sentences from dictation.

1. Vince was only thirteen when he went to work.
2. When he looked at the water, he thought about his mother.
3. The men enjoyed their short visits while the officers were selling their cargo.
4. While Vince was traveling home, he thought about the girl.

VI Modification: noun + '-ing' verb

Read sentence A. Use sentences 1 and 2 to make sentence 3.

Example:

    A. The worker was learning his job.
        1. Vince was a worker.
        2. He was learning his job.
            3. *Vince was a worker learning his job.*

Go on to Sentence B.

B. The people were speaking other languages.
    1. He listened to the people.
    2. They were speaking other languages.

      3. ....

C. The signalman was whistling signals.
    1. Vince listened to the signalman.
    2. He was whistling signals.

      3. ....

D. The prisoner was working in the prison.
    1. Vince was a prisoner.
    2. He was working in the prison.

      3. ....

E. The army officers were waiting on the dock.
    1. They were army officers.
    2. They were waiting on the dock.

      3. ....

F. The ship's officers were buying and selling cargo.
    1. They were ship's officers.
    2. They were buying and selling cargo.

      3. ....

VII Prepositions: review

Fill in the correct preposition. Use:

at   in   on   of

to   into   for   off

1. The old man is . . . . . the door.

2. Frank is . . . . . his car.

3. It's the third . . . . . May.

4. It's 11:44. We're leaving . . . . . 11:45. We're leaving . . . . . a minute.

5. The officers are coming . . . . . twelve o'clock.

6. Wait . . . . . an hour. The officers are coming . . . . . sixty minutes.

7. That's the army . . . . . the North.

8. They're bringing the gold. It's . . . . . the army . . . . . the South.

9. He was on the ship from May . . . . . October.

10. He was . . . . . the ship . . . . . six months.

11. Alice is ..... the refrigerator.
12. The money is ..... the plane trip.
13. He's leaving ..... the 23rd ..... May.
14. The ship is going to leave ..... six.
15. It's going to leave ..... three hours.
16. The crane takes the cargo ..... the dock.
17. It puts the cargo ..... the ship.
18. The ship is going to arrive ..... 3:00.
19. The crane takes the cargo ..... the ship. It puts the cargo ..... the dock.
20. The workers are putting the cargo ..... trucks.

answer key

Answers to comprehension questions are possible answers, though variations may be correct. Use short answers rather than complete sentences for oral work in the classroom.

NEXT MONDAY

II. 1. She was laughing because his uniform wasn't big enough.
  2. It was going to begin at 8:00.
  3. Frank's old army friends were going to be there.
  4. An old yellow piece of paper was in his pocket. It was a shoe repair ticket.
  5. A shoe repairman takes your shoes and gives you a ticket. He fixes your shoes. You give him the ticket and some money, and he gives you back your shoes.
  6. No. Frank was.
  7. He was repairing a shoe.
  8. They were there for twenty-eight years.
  9. No, they weren't.
  10. They were going to be ready the next Monday.

III. B. 1. He's at the bedroom door.
  2. She's at the kitchen table.
  3. He's at the car door.
  4. He's at his work table.
  5. She's at the window.

  C. 1. It doesn't begin at 9:00.
  2. They don't want to be there at 6:30.
  3. She doesn't want to go out at 8:00.
  4. He doesn't plan to be home at 8:00.

MAY TWENTY-THIRD

I. B. 3. a. wants
  b. stays
  c. reads

II. 1. No, she isn't.
  2. Everybody in town thinks she is ill.
  3. No, she isn't.

4. No, he doesn't.
5. Yes, he is.
6. He works at a small food store.
7. He doesn't want to be with his wife.
8. She plans to take Tom's money and leave him.
9. He plans to leave his wife and take a trip to Australia.
10. He puts it in five red books.
11. No, she doesn't.
12. No, he doesn't.
13. He wants to sell trash and old clothes.
14. She gives him Tom's red books and a lot of other things.
15. He's going to read them and then sell them. He's going to use the money in them, too.

III. A.
1. child
2. table
3. class
4. living room
5. birthday party

B.
1. It's for Alice.
2. It's for the old man.
3. It's for the trip.
4. It's for her breakfast.
5. It's for Tom.

C.
1. Is Alice giving things to the old man? Yes, she is.
2. Is Tom opening the book to page one? Yes, he is.
3. Is Tom giving much money to Alice? No, he isn't.
4. Is Tom planning a trip to Australia? Yes, he is.
5. Is Tom giving any food to the old man? No, he isn't.

D.
1. for fifteen hours
2. for seven hours
3. for seven days
4. for six months
5. for three hours

IV. A.
1. Tom goes home and sits down with one of his books.
2. He closes the book and puts it back.
3. Alice stays in bed and plans her trip.
4. He goes to work early and comes home late.
5. Every night Tom closes the store and puts some of the money in his pocket.
6. The old man comes into the store and asks for something to eat.
7. She's angry about the money and gives a lot of things to the old man.

B.
1. Alice's looking for the money and getting tired.

2. Tom's saving his money and planning a trip.
3. Tom's talking to the old man and getting angry.

V. A. 1. always
        2. sometimes
        3. never
        4. Sometimes
        5. always
        6. never
        7. always
        8. never

WHAT DIFFERENCE?

I. B. 1. noise
        2. robbery
        3. difference
        4. bank
        5. different
        6. teller   robber
        7. same
        8. accidents

II.   1. He gets up at 7:00 a.m.
        2. He's getting old. His hair isn't black now and he's getting a little fat.
        3. No, it isn't.
        4. Yesterday's clothes are on a chair. There are a lot of dishes on the table. The room isn't clean.
        5. He always has eggs, juice and tea.
        6. The cook in the restaurant calls, "Fire! Fire!"
        7. He finishes his breakfast. Then he leaves.
        8. He reads his newspaper.
        9. One car hits another car. The bus stops and all the people look at the accident. People run from the buildings to see it. Two police cars come and there is a lot of noise.
        10. A robber takes other people's money.
        11. He's a tall man. He's wearing black clothes and a black hat.
        12. No, he didn't.
        13. "Today there was a fire at a restaurant, a car accident, and a bank robbery."
        14. No. It wasn't interesting. It was like all his days.

III. B. 1. at 12:30
        2. at 9:15
        3. at 5:00
        4. at 9:00
        5. at 12:00
        6. at 10:45

IV. A. 1. He gets up and walks into the bathroom.
2. Then he stops and thinks, "I'm getting old."
3. Mr. Wilson opens the door of the restaurant and walks in.
4. He sits in the corner and doesn't look up.
5. He always sits down in the same seat and reads the newspaper.
6. He puts some money on the table and walks to the door.
7. The robber goes to the man at the window and gives him a piece of paper.

B. 1. Mr. Wilson leaves his desk, goes to another room and gets a cup of tea.
2. The robber gives him a piece of paper, takes the money and runs.
3. Mr. Wilson gets ready for bed, turns on the radio and listens to it.

V. A. 1. a lot of   5. a lot of
2. any   6. any
3. some
4. a little

B. 1. the same   4. the same
    no difference   no difference
2. different   5. different
    a difference   a difference
3. different   6. the same
    a difference   no difference

THE BEAUTIFUL SPY

I. B. 1. wrote   gave   4. ship   boat
2. took   South   5. prisons
3. knew   spy   6. Civil War

II. 1. They went to have a good time.
2. She served duck.
3. Her plan was to write a letter to the officers of the South, and to tell them about the North's plans.
4. She had the parties to learn their plans about the war.
5. The maid took it.
6. Seven people went to England. They were Mrs. Greenhow and six important men of the South. They went to get money for the South.

7. The plan was to use the small boat to leave the ship, buy some horses and ride back to the South.
8. Mrs. Greenhow took it. She put it under her clothes.
9. They didn't want the army of the North to see them.

III. A. 1. This is the seat of the chair.
How many seats does it have?
It has one seat.
2. This is the floor of the room.
How many floors does it have?
It has one floor.
3. This is the point of the pen.
How many points does it have?
It has one point.

B. 1. This is a window of the room.
How many windows does it have?
It has three windows.
2. This is a wall of the room.
How many walls does it have?
It has four walls.
3. This is a page of the newspaper.
How many pages does it have?
It has many pages.

C. 1. The army of the South was hungry.
2. The officers of the ship were having trouble, too.
3. The friends of the spy were officers.
4. The famous prisoner of the North was Mrs. Greenhow.
5. The people of the country were fighting.

D. 1. It's February 2nd.   3. It's July 7th.
2. It's March 31st.   4. It's May 1st.

IV. A. 1. The men laughed and had a good time.
2. She wrote a letter and gave it to her maid.
3. He asked a lot of questions and learned a lot about the spy.
4. They gave her a passport and said, "Don't come back!"
5. She went to a city in the South and waited and waited.

B. 1. Let's have dinner together and talk about our plans.
2. Let's stop Mrs. Greenhow's spying and put her in prison.
3. Let's take only a little of the money and leave in that small boat.

V. B. 1. know
      2. have
      3. come
      4. do
      5. go

6. write
7. give
8. take
9. think

A WORK OF ART

I. B. 1. walked
      2. put
      3. began

4. picked up
5. sat down
6. laughed

II. 1. T
    2. F
    3. F.
    4. T
    5. F
    6. F
    7. T

8. F
9. T
10. T
11. T
12. F
13. T
14. F

III. B. 1. Take Sasha's gift off the table, please.
       2. Take the newspapers and string off the chair, please.
       3. Take the statue off the desk, please.
       4. Take the lawyer's letter off the table, please.

IV. 1. thinking   put
    2. standing   went
    3. arrived   acting

4. laughing   asked
5. came   working

V. 1. Sasha
   2. Koshelkov
   3. Mrs. Smirnov

4. Ukhov
5. Shoshkin

THE WHISTLER

II. 1. Vince's family had very little money.
    2. No, he didn't.
    3. Vince left school when he was 13. The family needed money.
    4. He got a job at the dock.
    5. His sister needed expensive medicine.
    6. No, he wasn't.

7. It traveled to many countries from the north of Europe to the south.
8. Vince visited the countries.
9. A Civil War is a war between the people of the same country.
10. Army officers were on the dock.
11. He thought they wanted the ship's cargo.
12. They took them to a prison.
13. The army officers took them and wore them.
14. There are many answers. Examples:

They were going to fight with the ship's officers.
They were going to take the ship to the dock.
They were going to take the cargo off the ship.

15. He worked hard.
16. They used words from the two languages.
17. The ship came back. Men from the ship helped him.
18. He worked at the dock.
19. It is a big machine. It puts cargo on ships and takes it off ships.
20. He whistles signals and makes signals with his hands and arms to help the crane man use the crane.
21. He bought medicine and gifts for his family.
22. He wasn't happy about the girl — but he liked his work.

III. C.
1. into
in
2. into
in
3. into
in
4. into
in
5. into
in
6. into
in

IV.
1. Yes, he did.
2. No, he wasn't.
3. No, he wasn't.
4. Yes, he did.
5. Yes, they did.
6. No, it didn't.
7. Yes, there was.
8. Yes, they did.
9. No, they weren't.
10. No, she didn't.
11. Yes, it did.
12. No, he didn't.
13. Yes, it was.
14. Yes, he did.
15. Yes, he did.

VI. B.   He listened to the people speaking other languages.
    C.   Vince listened to the signalman whistling signals.
    D.   Vince was a prisoner working in the prison.
    E.   They were army officers waiting on the dock.
    F.   They were ship's officers buying and selling cargo.

VII.

1. at	11. at
2. in	12. for
3. of	13. on of
4. at in	14. at
5. at	15. in
6. for in	16. off
7. of	17. on
8. for of	18. at
9. to	19. off on
10. on for	20. into

vocabulary

This list includes all words used in *The Whistler* with the following exceptions: proper names, some grammatical terms used in titles of exercises, etc., abbreviations, contractions, and those lexical items commonly learned in sets—such as days of the week. (The sets and abbreviations are listed beginning on page 96.) The verbs are listed as base forms; however some other forms are included in the individual story lists. The vocabulary for the individual stories is cumulative, and is broken down into parts of speech beginning on page 90. The Checklist of Principal Structures, page 98, will provide additional help regarding the point of introduction of past tense verbs, etc.

a [1]
about [2]
accident [26]
act [55]
after [1]
again [14]
alarm clock [24]
all [1]
all right [26]
a lot of [3]
also [65]
always [3]
an [4]
and [1]
angry [13]
another [16]
answer *n.* [54]
answer *v.* [54]
any [2]
argue [54]
arm [52]
army [2]
army clothes [4]

army friends [1]
army job [2]
army officer [41]
army shoes [1]
army uniform [4]
around [25]
arrive [23]
art [52]
artist [56]
ask [14]
at [1]
at all [53]
at last [41]
at least [26]

back *adv.* [3]
back *n.* [3]
bad [26]
ball [28]
bank [26]
banking
 business [28]
bank robbery [27]

bathroom [24]
be [1]
beautiful [40]
because [12]
bed [12]
bedroom [1]
before [62]
begin [5]
believe [42]
between [44]
big [26]
birthday [56]
birthday party [18]
black [24]
blackboard [7]
boat [43]
book [14]
bottle [31]
boy [25]
bread [16]
breakfast [19]
bring [54]
brother [40]

brown [1]
building [2]
bus [26]
business [28]
busy [3]
but [2]
buy [13]
by [42]

cake [19]
call [25]
car [2]
car accident [27]
care [12]
cargo [63]
certainly [1]
chair [24]
child [18]
city [25]
civil war [40]
class [18]
clean [24]
clock [24]
close v. [13]
clothes [2]
cloud [62]
coat [18]
come [2]
complete [17]
conversation [37]
cook n. [25]
cook v. [64]
corner [25]
correct [17]
country [44]
crane [65]
crane man [65]
cry [43]
cup [33]

dad [62]
date [2]
day [2]
decide [42]
desk [6]
dessert [41]
difference [24]
different [24]
difficult [40]
dinner [16]
dinner party [40]
dinner table [41]
direction [38]
director [38]
dish [24]
do [1]
dock [62]
doctor [52]
dog [61]
door [1]
down [13]
drink [27]
drive [25]
dry [4]
duck [41]
during [40]

early [12]
earn [13]
earth [37]
eat [13]
education [53]
egg [25]
end n. [14]
engineer [60]
enjoy [40]
enough [3]
evening [42]

every [12]
everybody [13]
everything [62]
expensive [62]
eye [24]

family [56]
famous [40]
fast [25]
fat [1]
father [52]
feel [13]
few [2]
fight [40]
find [13]
find out [63]
finish [25]
fire [25]
fireman [4]
first [13]
fix [2]
floor [47]
flower [18]
food [12]
food store [12]
for [2]
foreign [64]
forget [40]
form n. [17]
friend [1]
from [2]
fruit [19]
full [43]
fun [61]

game [61]
get [1]

get up [14]
gift [53]
girl [17]
give [13]
glad [12]
glass [31]
go [1]
gold [42]
good [1]
goodbye [43]
good morning [54]
government [40]

hair [24]
half [32]
hand [52]
happy [14]
hard *adj.* [12]
hat [26]
have [1]
he [1]
hear [25]
heart [52]
heavy [43]
hello [2]
help *n.* [27]
help *v.* [27]
helper [65]
her [12]
here [2]
him [2]
his [1]
hit [26]
home [8]
horse [43]
hour [12]
house [14]
how [5]
hungry [25]

hurt [13]
husband [13]

I [1]
idea [53]
ill [13]
important [14]
in [1]
interesting [26]
into [1]
it [1]

job [2]
juice [25]

keep [4]
kind [16]
kitchen [1]
know [1]

land [42]
language [63]
last [41]
late [12]
laugh [1]
lawyer [54]
lazy [13]
learn [42]
least [26]
leave [12]
leg [47]
let [72]
let's go [25]
letter [41]
life [12]
live *v.* [12]

like *prep.* [27]
listen [3]
little [1]
live [2]
live *v.* [2]
living room [18]
long [13]
look [1]
look at [2]
look for [14]
love *n.* [13]
love *v.* [12]
lunch [32]

maid [41]
make [24]
man [2]
many [5]
me [2]
meat [16]
medicine [62]
metal [45]
milk [31]
minute [2]
Miss [60]
modern [45]
money [12]
month [20]
more [12]
morning [12]
mother [52]
mouth [55]
move [37]
much [13]
my [1]

name [2]
near [2]

necessary [53]
need [1]
never [2]
new [14]
news [26]
newspaper [26]
newspaperman [25]
next [1]
nice [12]
night [12]
no [8]
noise [25]
noon [20]
north [40]
northern [44]
not [12]
nothing [24]
now [1]
nurse [4]
nurse's uniform [9]

o'clock [1]
of [1]
of course [1]
off [58]
office [9]
office building [9]
officer [41]
often [54]
oh [1]
old [1]
on [2]
one [14]
only [12]
on time [17]
open *adj.* [1]
open *v.* [14]
or [14]
other [2]

our [26]
out [8]
over [43]
over there [43]

page [14]
paint [56]
painting [56]
pantomime [38]
paper [2]
park [61]
party [1]
pass [66]
passport [42]
pen [18]
pencil [58]
people [2]
pick up [53]
picture [56]
piece of [2]
plan *n.* [13]
plan *v.* [8]
plane [14]
plane trip [75]
play *n.* [38]
play *v.* [61]
please [43]
pocket [2]
point [47]
police car [26]
policeman [9]
police officer [9]
pour [69]
practice [65]
pretty [45]
prison [42]
prisoner [48]
problem [13]
put [13]

put on [13]

quarter [32]
question [41]

radio [27]
rain [42]
read [15]
ready [3]
red [14]
refrigerator [19]
remember [2]
repair [3]
repairman [2]
restaurant [25]
ride [43]
right [2]
ring [24]
rob [28]
robber [27]
robbery [27]
room [3]
rug [18]
run [25]

same [24]
save [12]
say [1]
school [61]
sea [43]
seat [26]
secretary [60]
see [1]
seem [26]
sell [14]
sentence [17]
serious [42]

serve [46]
she [1]
ship [42]
shoe [1]
shoe repair ticket [4]
short [63]
shower [24]
sick [12]
signal [65]
signalman [65]
sing [14]
sister [62]
sit [25]
sit down [14]
small [12]
so [26]
some [2]
something [12]
sometimes [13]
son [52]
soon [25]
sound [23]
south [40]
speak [38]
spy n. [40]
spy v. [42]
stand [1]
start [13]
statue [53]
stay [12]
still [2]
stop [24]
store [12]
story [19]
street [2]
string [53]
student [6]
study [20]
subject [17]
sun [37]

suppose [40]
sure [63]
swim [43]

table [6]
take [4]
take care of [12]
take off [58]
talk [2]
tall [25]
tea [25]
teacher [6]
tell [30]
teller [27]
terrible [54]
thank [52]
thanks [52]
thank you [52]
that [12]
the [1]
theater [55]
their [4]
them [1]
then [3]
there [2]
these [2]
they [2]
thing [2]
think [2]
this [2]
those [12]
ticket [2]
time [1]
tired [14]
to [1]
today [13]
together [50]
tomorrow [14]
tonight [1]

too [1]
town [13]
trash [14]
travel [42]
trip [12]
trouble [12]
truck [75]
try [9]
turn on [34]

under [43]
understand [53]
uniform [1]
up [14]
us [40]
use n. [16]
use v. [17]

vegetable [16]
very [2]
visit n. [63]
visit v. [42]

wait [20]
walk [1]
wall [48]
wallet [70]
want [1]
war [40]
water [31]
we [16]
wear [1]
weather [42]
week [14]
well expression [1]
well adj. [12]

well *adv.* [17]
what [1]
when [5]
where [1]
while [53]
whistle *n.* [65]
whistle *v.* [61]
white [4]
who [1]
why [1]
wife [12]

win [44]
window [6]
with [1]
woman [16]
wonderful [53]
word [16]
work *n.* [12]
work *v.* [2]
worker [28]
work of art [52]
work table *n.* [7]

world [26]
write [37]

year [1]
yellow [2]
yes [2]
yesterday [24]
you [1]
you know [1]
young [12]
your [1]

NEXT MONDAY

NOUNS

army	paper	
back	party	
building	people	
car	pocket	
clothes	room	
date	shoe	
day	street	
desk	student	
door	table	
friend	teacher	
home	thing	
job	ticket	
kitchen	time	
man	tonight	
minute	uniform	
name	window	
nurse	year	

NOUN COMPOUNDS

army clothes
army friend
army job
army shoes
army uniform
bedroom
blackboard
fireman
nurse's uniform
office building
policeman
police officer
repairman
shoe repair ticket
work table

VERBS

be	—doing	live	stand
—am	fix	look at	take
—are	get	need	talk
—is	go	plan	think
—was	have	remember	try
—were	—has	repair	walk
begin	keep	say	want
come	know	—said	wear
do	laugh	see	work
—does	listen to		

ADJECTIVES

brown	open
busy	ready
dry	right
fat	white
good	yellow
old	

ADVERBS

always	out
back	still
certainly	then
here	there
never	too
now	very
o'clock	

CONTRACTIONS

aren't	there's
doesn't	they're
don't	wasn't
he's	weren't
I'm	what's
it's	where's
she's	you're

NOUN DETERMINERS

a	a little
an	a lot of
any	
the	few
some	many
this	enough
these	next
	other
piece of	
all	

PREPOSITIONS

about	into
after	near
at	of
for	on
from	to
in	with

QUESTION WORDS

how	where
what	who
when	why

PRONOUNS

I, you, he, she, it, they
me, him, them,
my, your, his, their

CONNECTIVES

and   but
think (that)

EXPRESSIONS

Hello,	Well,
Of course,	Yes,
Oh,	No,
You know,	

vocabulary   91

MAY TWENTY-THIRD

NOUNS			VERBS	
bed	kind	sound	arrive	open
book	life	store	ask	put
bread	love	story	buy	put on
breakfast	meat	subject	close	read
cake	money	today	complete	save
child	month	tomorrow	earn	sell
class	morning	town	eat	sing
coat	much	trash	feel	sit down
dinner	night	trip	find	start
end	noon	trouble	get up	stay
flower	page	use	give	study
food	pen	vegetable	leave	take care of
form	plan	week	like	use
fruit	plane	wife	look for	wait
girl	problem	woman	love	
hour	refrigerator	word		
house	rug	work		
husband	sentence			

NOUN COMPOUNDS	ADJECTIVES		ADVERBS
birthday	angry	long	again
birthday party	correct	new	early
food store	glad	nice	first
living room	happy	red	late
	hard	sick	much
	hurt	small	on time
	ill	tired	sometimes
	important	well	up
	lazy	young	well

CONTRACTIONS

isn't   that's   who's

NOUN DETERMINERS	PRONOUNS	PREPOSITIONS
that	we	down
those	her	
a little more	everybody	
another	something	CONNECTIVES
every		
one		because
only		or
much		after
		know (that)

WHAT DIFFERENCE?

NOUNS			VERBS	
accident	dish	pantomime	call	ring
ball	earth	play	do	rob
bank	egg	quarter	—did	run
bottle	eye	radio	drink	seem
boy	fire	restaurant	drive	sit
bus	glass	robber	finish	speak
business	hair	robbery	hear	stop
chair	half	same	help	tell
city	hat	seat	hit	turn on
clock	help	shower	make	write
conversation	juice	sun	move	
cook	lunch	tea		
corner	milk	teller		
cup	news	water	CONTRACTIONS	
difference	noise	worker		
direction	nothing	world	here's	
director	office	yesterday	let's	

NOUN COMPOUNDS	ADJECTIVES	ADVERBS
alarm clock	bad	around
banking business	big	fast
bank robbery	black	so
bathroom	clean	soon
car accident	different	
newspaper	hungry	
newspaperman	interesting	
police car	tall	

PRONOUN	PREPOSITIONS	EXPRESSIONS
our	around	All right,
	like	At least,
		Let's go

THE BEAUTIFUL SPY

NOUNS

boat	land	question
brother	leg	rain
civil war	letter	sea
country	maid	ship
dessert	metal	south
duck	north	spy
evening	officer	wall
floor	point	war
gold	prison	weather
government	prisoner	while
horse		

VERBS

believe	serve
cry	spy
decide	suppose
enjoy	swim
fight	travel
forget	visit
learn	win
ride	

NOUN COMPOUNDS

army officer	dinner party
dinner table	passport

CONTRACTIONS

didn't	we're

ADJECTIVES		ADVERBS	PREPOSITIONS	
beautiful	modern	together	between	during
difficult	northern	over there	by	under
famous	pretty			
full	serious			
heavy				

PRONOUN	EXPRESSIONS	CONNECTIVE
us	at last	suppose (that)
	please	

A WORK OF ART

NOUNS			VERBS
answer	gift	pencil	act
arm	hand	picture	answer
art	heart	secretary	argue
artist	idea	son	bring
doctor	lawyer	statue	paint
education	Miss	string	pick up
engineer	mother	thanks	take off
family	mouth	theater	thank
father	painting	work of art	understand

ADJECTIVES	ADVERBS	PREPOSITION	CONNECTIVES
necessary	at all	off	when
terrible	often		while
wonderful			

EXPRESSIONS

Goodbye,   Good morning   Thank you,

THE WHISTLER

NOUNS		VERBS	ADJECTIVES
cargo	medicine	cook	expensive
cloud	park	find out	foreign
crane	school	pass	short
dad	signal	play	sure
dock	sister	pour	
dog	truck	practice	
fun	visit	whistle	**ADVERBS**
game	wallet		
helper	whistle		also
language	whistler		over there

NOUN COMPOUNDS	PRONOUN	CONNECTIVE
crane man	everything	before
plane trip		
signalman		

* * * * *

Days of the Week		Months of the Year		
Sunday	Thursday	January	May	September
Monday	Friday	February	June	October
Tuesday	Saturday	March	July	November
Wednesday		April	August	December

Common Abbreviations

Mr.	a.m.	etc.
Mrs.	p.m.	Dr.

Cardinal Numbers		Ordinal Numbers	
0	zero		
1	one	1st	first
2	two	2nd	second
3	three	3rd	third
4	four	4th	fourth
5	five	5th	fifth
6	six	6th	sixth
7	seven	7th	seventh
8	eight	8th	eighth
9	nine	9th	ninth
10	ten	10th	tenth
11	eleven	11th	eleventh
12	twelve	12th	twelfth
13	thirteen	13th	thirteenth
14	fourteen	14th	fourteenth
15	fifteen	15th	fifteenth
16	sixteen	16th	sixteenth
17	seventeen	17th	seventeenth
18	eighteen	18th	eighteenth
19	nineteen	19th	nineteenth
20	twenty	20th	twentieth
21	twenty-one	21st	twenty-first
22	twenty-two	22nd	twenty-second
23	twenty-three	23rd	twenty-third
24	twenty-four	24th	twenty-fourth
25	twenty-five	25th	twenty-fifth
26	twenty-six	26th	twenty-sixth
27	twenty-seven	27th	twenty-seventh
28	twenty-eight	28th	twenty-eighth
29	twenty-nine	29th	twenty-ninth
30	thirty	30th	thirtieth
40	forty	40th	fortieth
50	fifty	50th	fiftieth
60	sixty	60th	sixtieth
70	seventy	70th	seventieth
80	eighty	80th	eightieth
90	ninety	90th	ninetieth
100	one hundred	100th	one hundredth

checklist of principal structures
(structures are cumulative from one story to the next)

Story	Verb Structures	Noun Phrases (NP)	Adverbials	Coordinators & Subordinators	Other
Next Monday	(1) Verb BE: present and past • Used as copula in statements, etc. (*He's here*) and in question-word questions (*Where's my bat?*) • As auxiliary in present and past continuous: (*He's think-ing; She was talking.*) • As auxiliary in "going to" future (*He's not going to come; She wasn't going to tell me.*) (2) Verbs (*know, see, etc.*): present tense. • Affirmative, negative and in-terrogative (*They teach; I don't know; Do you like it?*) • Imperative: (*Come here!*)	• NPs used as sub-jects, objects and complements • Proper nouns (*Frank, Mary*) • Common nouns: mass and count (*shoes, paper*) • Pronouns: subject, object, possessive (*they, them, their, etc.*) • Noun compounds: (*bedroom, repairman, shoe repairman, army shoes, army uniform*)	• Adverbs: *certainly, still* • Adverbials of time: (*Now, in a few min-utes*) • Adverbials of place: (*here, at the door*) • Intensifier: *very* • Frequency adverb: *never*	• Coordinators: *and, but* • Subordinator: *that* [Verb *think* + (that) Sentence] (*I think that you have my shoes.*)	• Verb *say* + direct speech ("I didn't know," she said.)

Story	Verb Structures	Noun Phrases (NP)	Adverbials	Coordinators & Subordinators	Other
May Twenty-Third	• Verb + infinitive: *like, want, try, plan* (*He plans to leave; I don't want to go.*) • *There is/are:* (*There's some money on the table.*) • Two-word verbs: *put back, get up* (*He put the money back; She gets up at 10:00.*)	• Indefinite pronouns: *something, everybody* • Noun substitute: *much* (*He never gives her much.*) • Noun compound: *food store* • *It* in subject position (*It's time to look for it.*)	• NP + infinitive: *something to eat; time to go* • Indefinite pronoun + adjective: *something important* • Gerund phrase: *selling things is a lot of work; looking for the money was hard*	• Adverbials of time and place • Frequency adverbs: *sometimes, always* • Duration: *for (for fifteen hours)* • Intensifier: *so (so nice)*	• Subordinator: *that* [Verb *know* + (that) Sentence] (*I know there's some money.*) • Subordinator: *because* (*I went to bed because I was tired.*) • Subordinator: *after* (*He sells the books after he reads them.*)	• Verb *think* + direct speech ("*I'm lazy," he thinks.*) • Adjective + infinitive: *hard to see, glad to go, important to do*
What Difference?	• Two-word verb: *get up*	• Indefinite pronoun: *nothing* • Noun compounds: *alarm clock, bathroom, fireman, newsman, police car, policeman, car accident, bank robbery*	• Indefinite pronoun + adjective: *nothing interesting*	• Intensifier: *too* (*It's too big.*) • Adverb of manner: *fast* (*He drives fast.*)		• Verbs *call* and *ask* + direct speech ("*Is there any news?" be asks; The cook calls, "Fire!"*)

Story	Verb Structures	Noun Phrases (NP)	Adverbials	Coordinators & Subordinators	Other
The Beautiful Spy	• Past tense of regular verbs, affirmative, negative, interrogative • Irregular verbs: *go, come, have, do, know, write, eat, give, take, tell, say, think* • Verb + gerund: *enjoy (She enjoyed having parties.)* • Verb + infinitive: *decide, start (We decided to go.)* • *Let's* + verb *(Let's go; Let's not go.)* • Infinitive of purpose: *(Some came to forget the war.)*	• Noun compounds: *dinner party, dinner table, army officer* • Noun substitutes: *a lot, enough, more a little, all (He knew a lot; It wasn't enough. We took only a little.)*	• Intensifier: *so (I'm so tired.)*	• Subordinator: *that* [Verb suppose + (that) Sentence *(I suppose [that] he'll come.)*	• Echo construction: *(Her maid helped her and other people did, too.)* • Iteration: *we talked and talked, she waited and waited*
A Work of Art	• Past tense of irregular verbs: *put, begin, sit, bring* • Verb + infinitive: *begin (He began to open it.)* • Two-word verb: *pick up (He picked up the statue.)* • Infinitive of purpose: *(He went home to see his mother; I came to tell you.)*	• Noun compounds: *doctor's office, lawyer's office* • Appositives: *(Sasha, the only son,; Ukbov, the lawyer, ...)*	• Frequency adverb: *often*	• Subordinator: *while (I stood there while he opened the package.)* • Subordinator: *when (When the boy came the doctor was working.)*	• Echo constructions: *I'm so happy and my mother is, too; I didn't understand, but I know you do.* • Verb followed by infinitive with subject: *I want you to come; She wants me to keep it.*

Story	Verb Structures	Noun Phrases (NP)	Adverbials	Coordinators & Subordinators	Other
The Whistler	• Past tense of irregular verbs: *get, feel, buy* • Verb + infinitive: *learn (He learned to whistle.)* • Verbs + gerund: *like (He didn't like being on the ship.) think about (I thought about going.)* • Infinitive of purpose: *(I'm going there to look for a job.)*	• Noun compounds: *arm signal, signalman*		• Subordinator: *before (They got some of the money before the ship started...)*	• Iteration: *He tried and tried.*